I see all

Àngels Navarro

SALARIYA
BH
BOOK HOUSE

Mariona Cabassa

Two of these objects are not in the picture of the city.

Which ones?

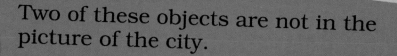

How many animals can you find?

What am I describing here?

Where are they hiding?

- Long ears and a very short tail.
- It turns when the wind blows.
- Be careful, it's prickly!
- As it grows, it faces the sun.

Are there more:

City signposts
or
Traffic lights
or
Traffic signs?

Additional spotting game: Look out for the black cat that appears in every scene!

Name ten objects in this picture that begin with the letter P.

Study the picture, cover it and answer these questions:

- Is there a dartboard near the mirror?
- Is there a violin in the room?
- Do the windows have curtains?
- Are there three goldfish in the bowl?

What am I?
My voice is tender, my waist is slender,
And I'm often invited to play.
Yet wherever I go, I must take my bow,
Or else I have nothing to say.

There are more animals than you think in this kitchen. Try to find all of them.

Combine the initials of four objects on the table to discover the cat's name.

There are six bottles. Can you find them and sort them into order of size?

It's Anna's 7th birthday and we've decided to throw a party for her. Before it starts, find all the objects that appear seven times.

Oh no! We've lost the matches, and can't light the candles on the cake. Can you find them?

Study the picture and find four objects that we can use to play games at Anna's birthday party.

Which of these objects are in the top half of the picture, which ones in the lower half, which ones are on the right or left hand sides of the page?

We are going bird watching in the park. Use these anagrams to help you find four different species.

PEMGAI

OSEOG

KDUC

NOEPGI

Can you find 12 orange objects?

Can you see where these bits and pieces belong in the picture?

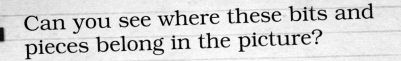

A number of objects have been lost in the waiting room. Use these clues to help the doctor find them.

- I am a brush, but not for your hair.
- My farmyard family is called a flock.
- I normally sit on top of the king's head.

Count how many red crosses there are.

Which one of these four circles do you need to eliminate so as to be left with three cars, three geese, three bears and six lollipops?

1.　　　　2.　　　　3.　　　　4.

Cross out all the letters that make up the words below. Unscramble the remaining letters to find out the name of the classroom.

Broom   Pencil   Orange

Scissors   Water   Mask

WMONIGRAMSOCEIBRAUAN
GRNKSLPISORTECNSESPESO

How many round things can you see? There are more than 15!

Four children can sit at each desk but there aren't enough chairs. How many chairs do we need so everyone can sit and work?

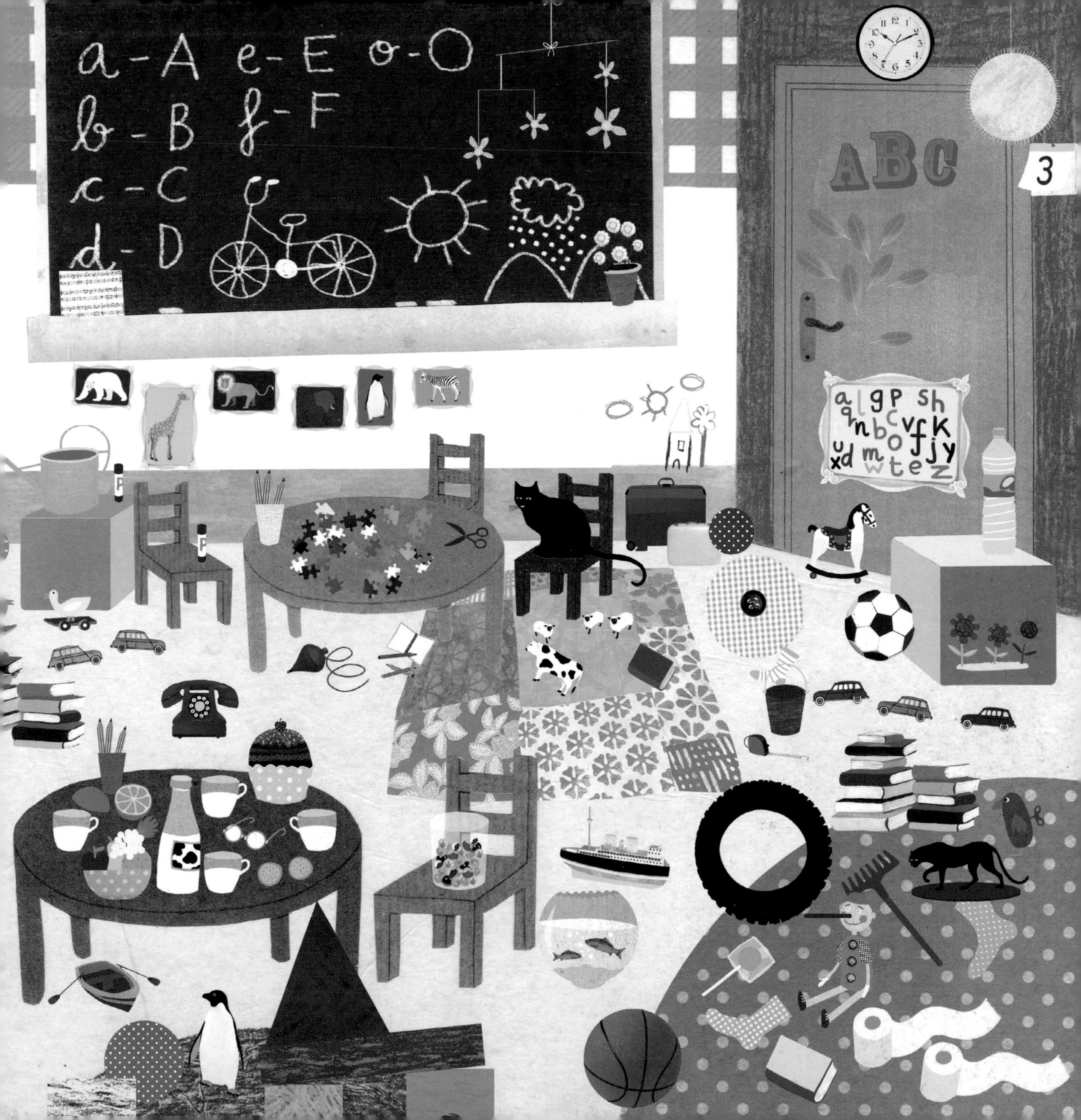

a-A e-E o-O
b-B f-F
c-C
d-D
ABC
3

How many hoops are there in the gym?

Do you know which sport each piece of equipment is used for?

Match up all the pairs of socks on the floor. Are there any odd ones?

The children have muddled up the names of the books they want. Can you help the librarian to sort out the right titles?

Alice	in Boots
Around the world	Island
Sleeping	in Wonderland
Puss	in Eighty Days
Treasure	Beauty

Find all these 'I like reading' symbols hidden around the library.

Can you re-arrange the encyclopaedias into alphabetical order? What letter should the first volume begin with? What letter should the last volume end with?

These objects are not quite the same as the ones on the farm. What is missing from each one?

Study the picture, cover it and answer these questions.

- What colour is the farmer's scarf?

- How many traffic signs are there?

So much noise! Do you know which animals make these sounds?

- Bleating

- Squealing

- Braying

- Crowing

- Barking

- Meowing

- Neighing

The text below is about the restaurant 'La Manduca'. Read it very carefully to find 10 mistakes.

La Mermelada is a luxury Indian restaurant which was founded by the cook's father over forty years ago. It is a very popular place to eat and is always packed with customers. Many famous people eat there and the walls are covered with signed photographs that they have given to the cook. The interior of the restaurant is beautifully decorated and the cook is famous for his vegetarian menu. He is a vegetarian himself and cannot bear to be near meat. In fact, he insists that his diet is so healthy that it is the reason he is still so slim. He is allergic to pollen so he never has flowers on the tables and always makes sure that the tables are set nicely and look very pretty. Although he is mostly in the kitchen he likes to look clean and smart at all times. His cat, 'Blackie', chases all the mice away. The restaurant is perfect in every way – no wonder it is so successful.

What do all these objects have in common? Are there any you could add to the list?

- Watering can
- Cup
- Fruit bowl
- Chest of drawers
- Bucket

Can you spot where these pieces fit in to the museum picture?

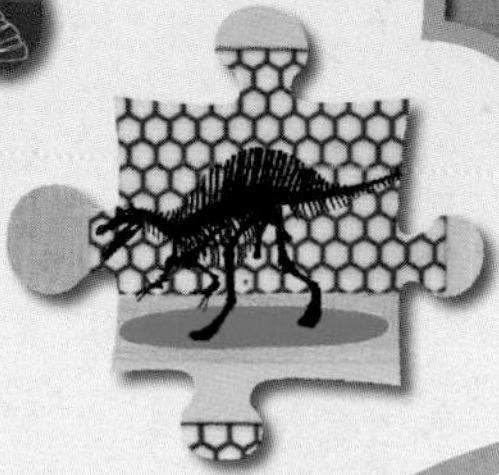

Can you find all the objects shown in silhouette here?

The list below contains seven objects that don't appear in the picture. Which ones?

- Cradle
- Grapes
- Washing machine
- Hive
- Bin
- Window
- Candlestick
- Fire extinguisher
- Key ring
- Xylophone
- Telephone
- Wheel
- Seal

Can you find six musical instruments in the theatre? Do you know what each one is called? Can you name any other musical instruments?

Which items in the picture could be stage costumes?

The show starts at 11 but the theatre is in such a mess! How much time is there to clean up?

What am I?
My first is in table but not in chair.
My second is in fire but not in wind.
My third is in eagle but never in flight.
My last is in hate, but also in love.
Hint: I make more rings the older I get.

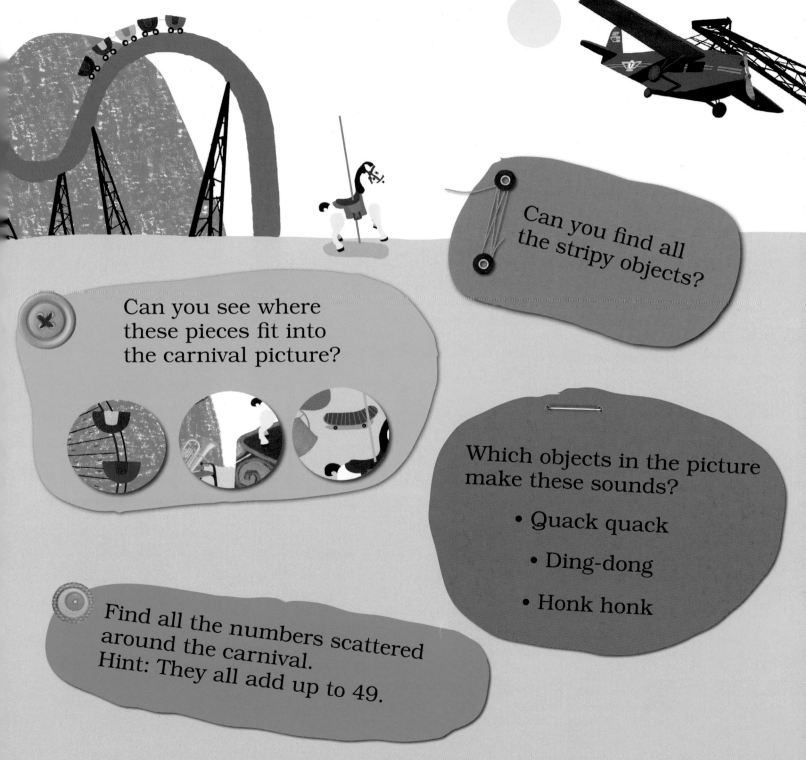

Can you find all the stripy objects?

Can you see where these pieces fit into the carnival picture?

Which objects in the picture make these sounds?

- Quack quack
- Ding-dong
- Honk honk

Find all the numbers scattered around the carnival.
Hint: They all add up to 49.

Lucy and her friends want to have a trip on the balloon, but there is a problem: the maximum weight must be less than 200 kg, or the balloon won't lift off. So, they can't bring all they want. They must bring the oxygen bottles, but what should be left behind?

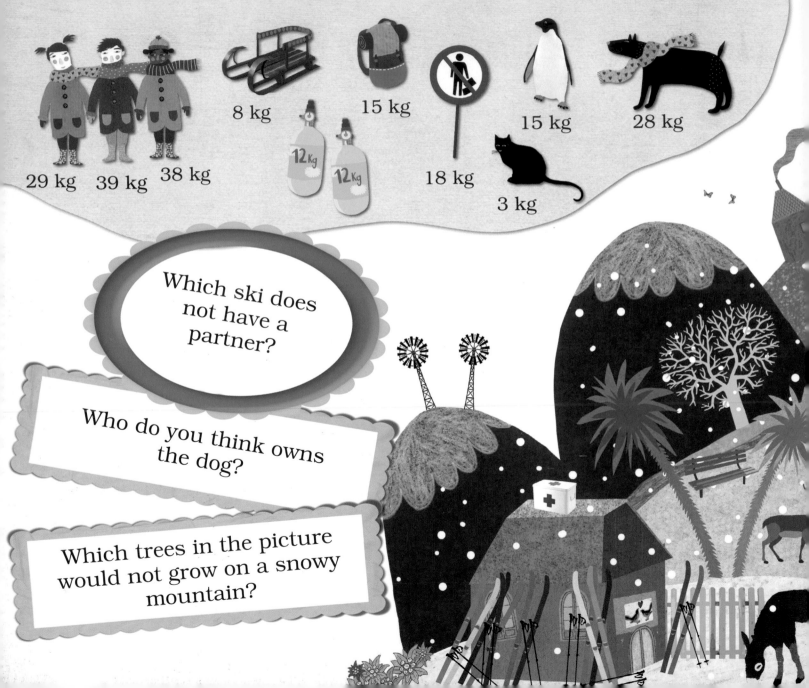

8 kg

15 kg

15 kg

28 kg

12 Kg

12 Kg

18 kg

29 kg   39 kg   38 kg

3 kg

Which ski does not have a partner?

Who do you think owns the dog?

Which trees in the picture would not grow on a snowy mountain?

STOP

There are many strange things in this wood. Can you find at least 12 things that you wouldn't find in any other wood?

Study the picture, cover it and answer these questions:

• What animals can you see?

• Who is sitting in the boat?

Find a mushroom identical to this one.

The reflection in the lake is not accurate. Can you spot eight differences?

Which animals in the zoo are pets, farm animals, wild animals, safari animals or sea creatures?

 Who do these tails belong to?

 How many toy animals are there in the picture?

Each clue identifies an animal in the picture. Can you find them?

- It's known as the king of the savannah.
- It looks like it's wearing grandpa's pjs.
- It can change colour whenever it likes.
- It has the largest nose.
- It can walk, trot or gallop.
- It's first up in the morning.
- It likes to keep cool.

The letters hidden in the forest spell out a word that tells you how the explorer got here.

There are five different suitcases in the circus picture.

- Which suitcase is the nearest to the leopard?
- What colour is the smallest suitcase?
- Which suitcase is the largest?

The trapeze artist, the strong man and the ringmaster need to put on the rest of their costumes. Can you find what they need?

Name everything you see that gives off light.

Which circus animal could have left these prints?

Find all the objects at the airport that have wheels.

'We would like to inform all passengers that they must find ten objects with the same pattern before boarding their plane.'

Which passengers do you think come from non-European countries? Why?

The train isn't the only means of transport in this station. Can you find them all?

There are so many suitcases scattered about! How many can you spot?

Do you think it's daytime or nighttime?

There are some very strange things in this camp site that you wouldn't find in any other. Can you spot them?

There are two identical objects that will protect your skin from the sun. Can you find them?

Find all these objects in the picture. What do they all have in common?

- Plane
- Gloves
- Backpack
- Bin
- Bucket
- Washing machine
- Trailer
- Tent
- Cool box
- Flippers
- Trainers

Footwear ... in all shapes and sizes!
Put them all into pairs.

Which animals are not
in their natural habitat?

Find at least ten things
that begin with the letter S.

Find six objects that
help you to see better.

BAR

OFFER

OFFER

RCALEE

TAASP

EIRC

FPEMREU

UCEIJ

What is inside the cardboard boxes at the supermarket? Unscramble the letters to find out.

Match up each fruit with a number (see key below). Add up each row across and each column down.

🍎 = 2   🍍 = 6   🍎 = 3   🍌 = 4   🍓 = 7

					14
					22
24		21			

Only one of these shapes folds up to match the one in the toy shop. Which one?

Which letter is missing from the ABC poster on the wall?

Which objects in the toy shop do each of these keys unlock? Hint: Look carefully at the shape of the keys.

You want to buy presents for three friends, but you only have £10. What could you buy?

£3

£7

£5

£1.50

£1.50

£1.50

£1.50

This is the largest shopping centre in town. Everyone knows that they can find anything they need here... but do they have everything on our list?

- Toaster
- Ice cream
- Coffee pot
- Garden rake
- Fruit
- Umbrella
- Saw
- Frying pan
- Phone

- Balloon
- Cake
- Baby's bottle
- Spinning top
- Iron
- Wheel
- Hot water bottle
- Table tennis bats
- Tutu

Solutions

Spread 1
Game 1
Snake and aubergine.

Game 2
There are 31 animals.

Game 3
- Rabbit
- Windmill
- Cactus
- Sunflower

Game 4
There are two city signs, one traffic sign and four traffic lights.

Spread 2
Game 1
Present, pencils, piano, perfume, parasol, Pinocchio, panther, poster, puzzle pieces, picture…

Game 2
- Are there three goldfish in the bowl? No
- Do the windows have curtains? No
- Is there a violin in the room? Yes
- Is there a dartboard near the mirror? No

Game 3
A violin.

Spread 3
Game 1
Cat, caged bird, sardines, octopus, cockroaches, worm in the apple, chicken egg-basket, butterflies on the tureen, fly, birds on the fridge, lizard, donkey.

Game 2
The cat's name is 'Paws'. The four objects are: pegs, aubergine, water bottle, scales.

Game 3
See image below.

Spread 4

Game 1
Paper snakes, candles, paper birds, gift boxes, stripy cups.

Game 2
The matchbox is on the shelves beside a paper bird.

Game 3
Marbles, playing cards, dice and skittles.

Spread 5

Game 1
Top half: Sun, houses, parachute, kite.
Lower half: Flower, geese, fish.
Right: Sun, kite, fish.
Left: Parachute, milk, flowers, geese.

Game 2
Magpie, duck, goose, pigeon.

Game 3
Tennis racket, gnome's hat, wheelbarrow, tricycle, bucket, playground slide, flippers, house, oranges, rugby ball, signpost, flowers.

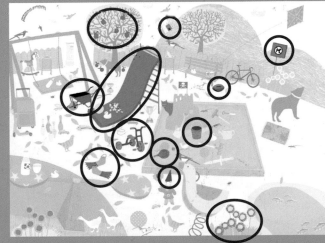

Spread 6

Game 1
See image.

Game 2
Toothbrush, sheep, crown.

Game 3
There are 11 red crosses.

Game 4
Eliminate the second circle.

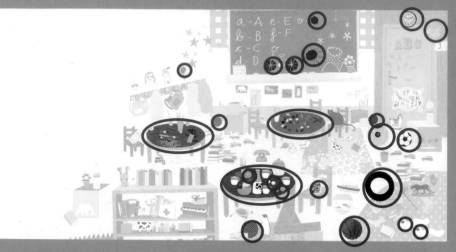

Spread 7

Game 1
The classroom name is *Penguins*.

Game 2
See image.

Game 3
Seven more chairs are needed.

Spread 8

Game 1
There are eight hoops.

Game 2
Roller skating, hurdles, weightlifting, basketball, skiing, cycling, table tennis, archery, football, gymnastics.

Game 3
See image below.

Spread 9

Game 1
Alice in Wonderland
Around the World in Eighty Days
Sleeping Beauty
Puss in Boots
Treasure Island

Game 2
See image.

Game 3
See image below.

Spread 10

Game 1
See image.

Game 2
- There are two traffic signs.
- The scarf is red with orange stripes.

Game 3
Bleating: sheep
Squealing: pig
Braying: donkey
Crowing: cockerel
Barking: dog
Meowing: cat
Neighing: horse

Spread 11

Game 1
- The restaurant is called 'La Manduca', not 'La Mermelada'.
- The founder was a woman.
- There isn't a single customer around.
- There are no signed photographs.
- The cook is near meat.
- The cook isn't slim.
- There are flowers on the tables.
- The tables are not set nicely.
- The cook is not clean and smart.
- There are mice in the restaurant.

Game 2
See image.

Game 3
All five objects are blue. The fish tank, cook's shirt, bottle rack, wall, skateboard and one wine cup are also blue.

Spread 12

Game 1
See image.

Game 2
See image.

Game 3
Cradle, washing machine, wheel, bin, key ring, xylophone, seal.

Spread 13

Game 1
Musical instruments: violin, cello, drum, piano, accordion, tuba.

Game 2
Necklace, pendant, sombrero, mask, crown, socks, Indian feather headdress, sunglasses, ballerina dress, jacket, shoes, blouse, the clothes in the trunk...

Game 3
The clock is at 10.10, so there is only 50 minutes to clear up.

Game 4
The tree.

Spread 14

Game 1
See image.

Game 2
See image.

Game 3
• Duck
• Bell
• Horn

Game 4
The numbers: 18 + 13 + 4 + 2 + 10 + 2 = 49

Spread 15

Game 1
For the balloon to lift off the traffic sign must be left behind. Adding together all the weight equals 217 kg. By leaving the traffic sign (18 kg), the balloon will be able to take off carrying 199 kg.

Game 2
See image.

Game 3
The dog is wearing the same coloured scarf as Lucy, so she is probably its owner.

Game 4
See image.

Spread 16

Game 1
Picture of shoes, starfish, lamp on top of tree, suitcase, harp, gift box, Viking helmet, painting on tree, lion mask, caged banana, tree with electric cable, rocking horse, flying seahorses, hopscotch drawn on grass, colander on top of tree, cat on treetop, telephone.

Game 2
- Nobody is sitting in the boat.
- Butterflies, birds, rabbit, deer, horse, cat, turtle, seahorse, starfish, stork, wolf, snails.

Game 3
See image.

Game 4
See image.

Spread 17

Game 1
Pets: Cat.
Farm: Cow, rabbit, sheep, goose, donkey, cockerel.
Wild: Wolf, birds, deer, squirrel.
Safari: Monkey, crocodile, elephant, giraffe, lion, zebra, snakes, chameleon.
Sea: Whale, fish, seahorse, pelican, crabs, penguins, seal.

Game 2
See image.

Game 3
There are eight toy animals.

Game 4
Lion, zebra, chameleon, elephant, horse, cockerel, polar bear.

Spread 18

Game 1
Cat, dog, duck, caged bird, goldfish, octopus, whale, sheep, pig, crab, cockerel.

Game 2
See image.

Game 3
Plane.

Spread 19

Game 1
- The orange
- The green
- The pink.

Game 2
The trapeze artist's tutu. The ringmaster's jacket. The strong man's stripy body suit.

Game 3
Fire, moon, stars, lamp post, trailer lamp, torch, sun, spotlights, candles, string of light bulbs.

Game 4
The polar bear.

Spread 20

Game 1
Planes, suitcases, skates, toy car, hoover, baggage trunk, tricycle, toy horse.

Game 2
See image.

Game 3
The four passengers at the front are wearing traditional costumes from non-European countries.

Spread 21

Game 1
See image.

Game 2
There are 23 suitcases, (two are on the toy car).

Game 3
The clock is at 10:10 and all the street lamps are lit, so it's nighttime.

Spread 22
Game 1
Chandelier, giraffe, paper boats in the sea, coatstand with hat and stick, computer screen, erupting volcano, traffic lights in the middle of the field, washing machine. (The drill, the bucket and mop are things one can find as part of campsite facilities).

Game 2
See image.

Game 3
These objects are all meant to have something put inside them.

Spread 23
Game 1
See image.

Game 2
Pig, crocodile, monkey, buffalo, cat, duck, tropical birds.

Game 3
Shoes, seahorse, stripy jumper, sun lotion, sandal, slipper, seagull, sandcastle, sunflower, sunglasses, sea, sand, ship, starfish, skates...

Game 4
See image.

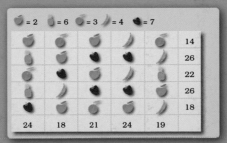

Spread 24
Game 1
Perfume, rice, pasta, cereal, juice.

Game 2
Tuba, monkey, diving helmet, backpack, wheel, robin, Viking helmet, pipe, goose, radio, phone, trees, cat, sunflowers, plants, giraffe, slippers, frying pan.

Game 3
See image.

Spread 25

<u>Game 1</u>
The first cube

<u>Game 2</u>
The missing letter is 'e'.

<u>Game 3</u>
See image.

<u>Game 4</u>
You could buy:
- a kite and two puppets
- three puppets
- a scooter and two puppets
- a spinning top, a scooter and a puppet.

Spread 26

<u>Game 1</u>
No, there is no: toaster, fruit, ice cream, balloon, baby's bottle, hot water bottle.

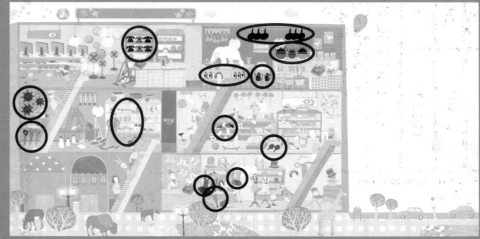